The Red Sea

AN ASTRONAUT'S VIEW OF THE RED SEA FROM GEMINI 12

FRANCINE JACOBS

The Red Sea

ILLUSTRATED BY ELSIE WRIGLEY

William Morrow and Company   New York 1978

Library of Congress Cataloging in Publication Data

Jacobs, Francine.
  The Red Sea.

  Summary: Discusses the corals, animal life,
mineral resources, and history of the strategic waterway
dividing Africa from the Arabian peninsula.
   1. Red Sea—Juvenile literature. [1. Red Sea]
I. Wrigley, Elsie.   II. Title.
GC741.J32   500.9′165′33   77-25927
ISBN 0-688-22150-5
ISBN 0-688-32150-X lib. bdg.

Printed in the United States of America.
First Edition
1   2   3   4   5   6   7   8   9   10

The author wishes to thank
Doctor David Ross, Associate Scientist,
Woods Hole Oceanographic Institution,
for reading and checking the manuscript of this book.

For my Monday morning friends,
with affection.

Contents

I An Unusual Sea 11

II A Strategic Waterway 15

III The Varied Corals 27

IV Life on the Reef 39

V Mineral Resources 59

VI An Ocean Being Born 69

Index 77

I

An Unusual Sea

Rays of shimmering light rise from the surface of
the water. Beneath the torrid, blazing sun, a ship
sails the brilliant, clear waters of this coral sea.
It is a sea steeped in history yet little understood.
Below the shining surface of the waves lurk
treacherous reefs and strange, unexplained
currents. Still deeper in the depths lie treasures of
untold value. Suddenly a sailor cries out,

warning all to take cover. The *khamsin*, the seasonal wind, is about to engulf the ship in a blinding, whipping sandstorm, even though it is many miles from land. The ship is journeying on perhaps the most unusual body of water on the face of the earth, the Red Sea.

The Red Sea divides the barren desert wastes of Egypt, Sudan, and Ethiopia in East Africa from those of Saudi Arabia and Yemen in Asia. A narrow, deep canyon of water about the size of California, it stretches northward from the Indian Ocean like an upraised arm with two fingers extended, forming a V at the top. The finger to the west is the Gulf of Suez, which is joined by the Suez Canal to the Mediterranean Sea. The other, to the east, is the Gulf of Aqaba. To the south, the Red Sea ends at the narrow Straits of Bab-el-Mandeb, which forms an elbow connecting it to the Gulf of Aden.

The waters of the Red Sea are among the saltiest and hottest on earth; their temperature ranges from 70 degrees to 94 degrees Fahrenheit. The sea usually appears a clear blue green, but at certain seasons, when conditions are right, microscopic floating plants called "algae" may flourish. Normally blue green, the blooms of the

12

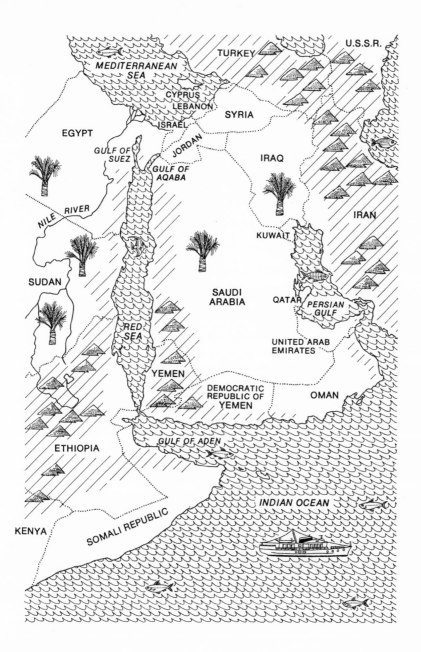

algae turn reddish brown when dying, like leaves in the fall, making the sea appear red. This is the reason, scientists believe, it was named the Red Sea.

The Red Sea has played a vital role in world history. The vessels of the Egyptian pharaohs sailed its waters laden with riches. It is famed in the Bible as the sea through which Moses led the children of Israel. In modern times, the Red Sea has been the focus of great political and economic interest.

In addition to being a strategic waterway, the Red Sea is an extraordinary marine habitat, which hosts an unusual and unique community of sea life. It is also a geologic wonder. A crack in the surface of the planet runs up its center, splitting the sea bottom. With its seabed slowly widening, the Red Sea is in the process of becoming an ocean.

II

A Strategic Waterway

The Red Sea, one of the first major bodies of water to be referred to in history, was an important link between ancient civilizations. Despite the barren deserts around it, mariners of long ago braved its treacherous reefs in pursuit of trade.

About five thousand years ago, when the first pyramids were built, Egypt already had a thriving

15

agriculture. The Egyptians were using the Red Sea as a trade route to obtain gold, ivory, ebony, cinnamon, skins, and the precious substances of frankincense and myrrh. These were burned as incense in the temples because of their pleasant fragrances. The gummy resin of myrrh was also used in perfumes, lotions, medicines, and in fluids to preserve the bodies of mummies.

The Egyptians inscribed evidence of this thriving commerce on the Red Sea on a black stone tablet, which is exhibited today in the National Museum of Archeology in Palermo, Italy. This tablet, known as the Palermo Stone, records an ambitious trade mission launched by the Egyptian Pharaoh Sahure around 2950 B.C.

Sahure dispatched eight vessels, which sailed down the Red Sea, and perhaps through the Gulf of Aden and into the Indian Ocean, to the mysterious land of Punt. The whereabouts of Punt is uncertain. Some scholars believe that the ancient Egyptians may have called all of southern Arabia and much of East Africa Punt.

Around 1500 B.C., Queen Hatshepsut of Egypt also sponsored an epic voyage to Punt via the Red Sea. She had the story of the journey illustrated and recorded in a series of colored reliefs and hieroglyphs, or picture writing, on the terraced walls of a temple near the ancient Egyptian city of Thebes. The detail in these pictures and inscriptions is remarkable.

We see the queen and her people bidding

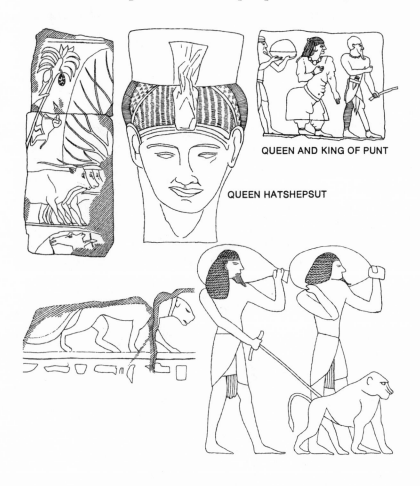

QUEEN AND KING OF PUNT

QUEEN HATSHEPSUT

PICTURES ON EGYPTIAN-TEMPLE WALLS OF EXPEDITION TO PUNT

farewell to the fleet of five ships, the square-rigged galleys on their way, the wind filling their sails, and the sailors toiling at their oars. Pictures show the marine life in the Red Sea at that time, including shellfish, squid, and some thirty different kinds of reef fish. Other illustrations depict the travelers in the land of Punt. It is a marshy place

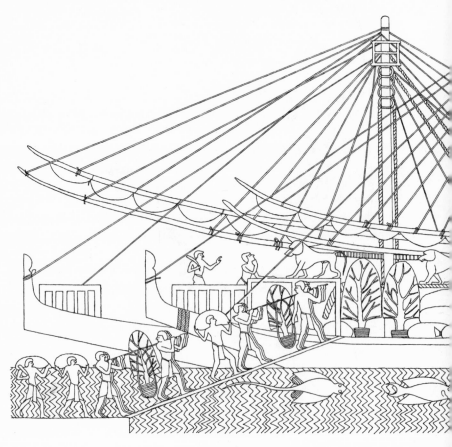

LOADING THE SHIP IN PUNT

with animals, grassy huts, and trees. They are
welcomed by a fat queen, a king, and long-haired
warriors. Finally, we see the return of the
expedition and the unloading of the precious
cargo. There are myrrh trees in tubs for the great
temple, live apes, monkeys, dogs, leopard skins,
cinnamon wood, ivory, gold, and silver.

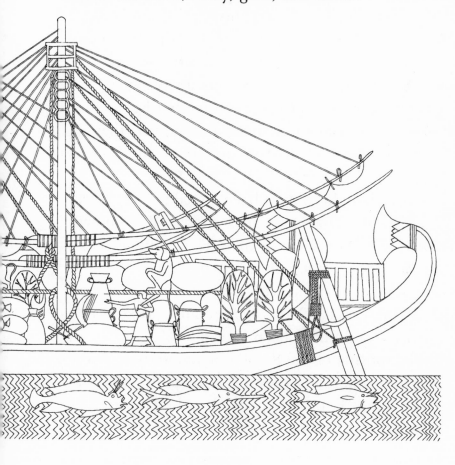

The ancient Israelites, however, were the ones responsible for making the Red Sea famous. The most celebrated event in history for which the Red Sea is known is the description in the Bible of its crossing by the Israelites on their flight from bondage in Egypt. While scholars debate the date of this event, many place it in the thirteenth century B.C. Exodus, the second book of the Old Testament, records that the Hebrews, led by Moses, safely crossed the waters of the Red Sea, which divided for them and then rushed together to drown the pursuing Egyptians.

Many historians now believe, however, that Moses did not lead the Israelites across the Red Sea proper but rather through the Reed Sea, which is thought to have been a reed marsh located where the Suez Canal is today. It is known that Greek translators of the Old Testament in the third century B.C. mistranslated a Hebrew phrase *Yam* meaning "sea" and *suph* meaning not "red" but "reed." *Yam suph* became "Red Sea" when it should have been "Reed Sea."

The fording of the Reed Sea is more likely to have occurred than a crossing through the Red Sea to the south. Experts explain that the Hebrews departed in haste from a point to the west on

MOSES LEADING THE ISRAELITES ACROSS THE RED SEA

the Nile Delta. They traveled on foot and donkey eastward, seeking to escape from Egypt on their journey to Canaan, the Promised Land. The shortest route would place the Reed Sea in their path. They may have been aided in their crossing by fierce, changing winds and shifting tides, which caused the waters to recede temporarily.

At the time of the Exodus, just to the north of the Promised Land of Canaan, along the coast of the eastern Mediterranean, were numerous city-states. They occupied areas that today are in Israel, Lebanon, and Syria. In these tiny kingdoms dwelt the Phoenicians.

The Phoenicians were outstanding seamen and traders, who knew the Red Sea well. These merchantmen grew wealthy selling cloth, which they had learned to dye reddish purple with an extract from sea snails. They established a port on the eastern arm of the Red Sea, on the Gulf of Aqaba, at the site of the modern Israeli harbor of Elat. From this harbor, they traded for themselves and for other nations. It is recorded that around 950 B.C., Israel's King Solomon prevailed upon the neighboring Phoenician king, Hiram of Tyre, to build ships and launch a joint expedition down the Red Sea to Ophir. The location of

Ophir, like that of the fabled Punt, remains a secret.

Some historians believe that increasing trade on the Red Sea prompted the Queen of Sheba, whose kingdom was supposedly Yemen, on the southwestern Arabian coast, to make her celebrated visit to King Solomon. Perhaps she came to negotiate trade agreements, for Solomon's ships were interfering with her commerce. His ships crossed the Red Sea between Arabian and Ethiopian ports so much faster than the queen's camel caravans could make the overland journey that her economy was suffering.

More than three centuries later, the Red Sea had a role in what was perhaps the most daring and adventurous maritime voyage in all of history. About 600 B.C., an Egyptian pharaoh, Necho II, was determined to find a route that would circle Africa to the Mediterranean. Several times before in antiquity, as far back as 3500 years earlier, waterways had been constructed by pharaohs connecting the Red Sea to the Mediterranean, usually via the Nile River. These waterways were early versions of today's Suez Canal. Necho had wanted to reopen such a canal, but he had been warned that the Persians, his enemies in the east, might take advantage of it.

Because of their seafaring knowledge, Necho engaged Phoenicians to find an alternate route. The expedition, as described 150 years later by a Greek historian and geographer named Herodotus, was comprised of several ships. No one in the ancient world knew the dimensions of Africa, but it was undoubtedly believed to be much smaller than it is. The fearless Phoenicians started by sailing south in a clockwise direction through the Red Sea, down and around the tip of Africa, up the continent's Atlantic coast, through the Straits of Gibraltar and the Mediterranean Sea, arriving back in Egypt. Their incredible journey took them three years, during which they sailed and rowed 13,000 miles through strange and uncharted seas.

So remarkable was their achievement that Herodotus himself had difficulty believing it. What confused him was that the Phoenicians reported the sun's passing to their right, or north, below the equator in the southern hemisphere. These observations did not agree with the path of the sun in the northern hemisphere. We are indebted to Herodotus for recording his doubts since they lend validity to the Phoenicians's feat.

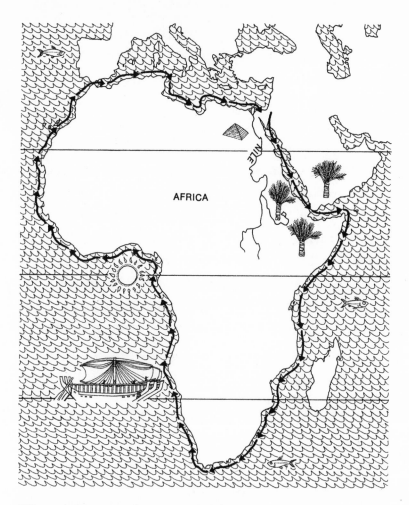

The circumnavigaton of Africa is not known to have been repeated again for more than 2000 years until Portuguese explorers, sailing counterclockwise, almost accomplished it in the fifteenth century A.D.

During this long period of time, trade between the peoples of the Mediterranean region and those of Asia became increasingly important. The value of the Red Sea as a passageway for commerce increased. Pepper, dyes, silk, ivory, perfumes, and precious stones from Arabia, India, the island of Ceylon, and other parts of Asia attracted the Greeks and later the Romans.

There was no direct passage between the Mediterranean and the Red Sea, however, so goods had to be transported over land between them. Not until the construction of the Suez Canal in modern times did the Red Sea achieve its great importance in commerce and become one of the world's most strategic waterways.

III

The Varied Corals

The Red Sea is a most unusual marine habitat.
It is a great trough of hot, salty seawater fed by
the Indian Ocean through the narrow straits of
Bab-el-Mandeb. In these channels lies a shallow
undersea shelf, which acts like a dam keeping
back cold water from the depths. Only warmer
surface inflows enter the Red Sea. There, heated
by the burning rays of the tropical sun, the

27

temperature at the surface may reach 94 degrees Fahrenheit. The high water temperature and the dryness of the desert atmosphere account for an astounding evaporation of some eighty inches of water a year. The loss of these billions of gallons annually is made up from the inflows.

The excessive evaporation of the surface water has another effect. It leaves behind such a large residue of salt that the Red Sea has one of the highest salt concentrations on earth. Its salinity is high also because of the sparse rainfall and the absence of inflowing rivers, which would provide fresh water to dilute it. Seawater averages about 35 parts of salt to 1000 parts of water. Red Sea water has 40 or more parts per 1000.

The Red Sea lies in a warm belt that circles the globe between latitudes 30 degrees north and 30 degrees south. Between these latitudes, at the center of which lies the equator, seawater rarely falls much below 72 degrees Fahrenheit. In the shallow waters of this zone, coral-producing creatures live and form reefs.

The word *coral* comes from the Greek *korallion*, which means "red coral." The Greeks may have taken this term from the language of ancient peoples who lived near the Red Sea.

Ancient peoples considered the corals to be trees with limbs and the tiny coral creatures to be their blossoms. Until the eighteenth century even learned scientists believed that corals were sea trees. Today corals are known to be really moving, feeding, growing, and reproducing animals.

Related to jellyfish and to the flowerlike sea anemones, which are commonly found rooted to the sea floor, corals are fragile animals. Their soft bodies are called "polyps." A coral polyp may live singly or in groups joined together in colonies. Some corals secrete a limestone skeleton around them as hard as stone; these are the reef builders. Others produce a hornlike material. These types, the so-called soft corals, are the lacy sea fans and frondlike sea whips and sea feathers.

Underwater, slow-motion films show the true animal characteristics of corals. The polyps, which vary greatly in shape, unfold, stretch, sway, and bend, extending delicate, stinging, feeding tentacles. They move in an exquisitely graceful ballet, seizing microscopic creatures that drift by. Reef-building corals also take nourishment from algae that live among their polyps.

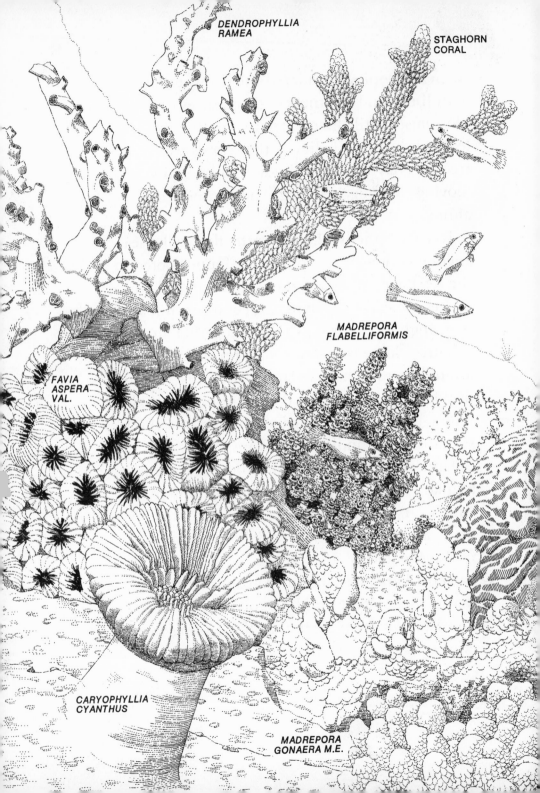

DENDROPHYLLIA
RAMEA

STAGHORN
CORAL

FAVIA
ASPERA
VAL.

MADREPORA
FLABELLIFORMIS

CARYOPHYLLIA
CYANTHUS

MADREPORA
GONAERA M.E.

BLACK CORAL

ALCYONARIAN
FORMATION

BRAIN CORAL

SEA
WHIPS

MUSHROOM
CORAL

The corals in the Red Sea are wondrous and varied. The amount of sunlight that filters down to them tends to determine their kind and size. The underwater world resembles an exquisite sea garden, where divers and snorkelers are treated to magnificent sights. There are corals of all sizes, shapes and colors: red, purple, pink, yellow, and tan. The brilliantly colored, soft feather and fan corals gently sway in the currents. The shapes of corals often give them their popular names. Among the hard corals, the brain coral with its lobular, grooved surfaces is easy to identify; so are the single giant mushroom corals, the staghorns, elkhorns, countless fingers, and packs of cards.

Reef-building corals thrive in the Red Sea. Their hard, limestone skeletons accumulate like stacks of cups, one upon the other. Many layers of living corals build on the skeletons of dead corals and create the coral reefs. Treacherous reefs, which rise to within a few feet of the surface, fringe almost the entire seacoast. And because of them only a small number of seaports exist. Reefs have multiplied and spread to such an extent that they now obstruct the once-flourishing port of Suakin on the Sudanese coast. Suakin today is a

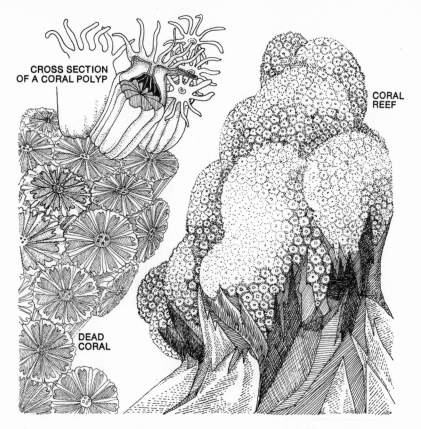

CROSS SECTION
OF A CORAL POLYP

CORAL
REEF

DEAD
CORAL

ghost town, with its homes empty and falling into
disrepair, a victim of the corals. These fringing
reefs stretch for nearly a thousand miles, extending in parallel lines off both coasts.

A second set of coral reefs, farther from the
coasts, occur more irregularly and are separated
from the fringing reefs by channels. These
offshore reefs sit upon huge underwater banks,

33

which plunge to great depths. In the middle and southern sectors of the Red Sea, some reefs protrude just above the surface, forming small, mostly barren coral islands—nesting places for seabirds and turtles. Only the channel running up the center of the Red Sea between the offshore reefs is safe for large ships to navigate. This channel is over one hundred miles wide in places.

The coral reefs of the Red Sea are said to contain more limestone than all the buildings of Europe and North America combined. The reefs of the Red Sea resemble cities, teeming with life like great urban centers. Millions of creatures live in these cities, finding shelter in their cracks and crannies, winding passages, deep caves, and grottoes. There they find food, mates, and protected nooks, which serve as nurseries for their young.

But these reefs also serve other important functions. They act as breakwaters, sparing the shore from erosion, protecting and preserving the coastline. They create tidal pools, sheltered bays, and inlets, where sea plants and shore animals, such as snails and crabs, live. They are habitats for fish and shellfish. The reefs are important links in the universal food chain. Hungry predator fish visit the reefs to feed, and they, in turn, are eaten by other larger fish in the open sea, which are then eaten by people.

Life in the Red Sea depends upon the complex relationships that exist among the plants, corals, and other animals. A team of biologists recently demonstrated the destructive effect pollutants have on corals. In the Gulf of Aqaba off the Red Sea port of Elat, they studied two stretches of reef—one polluted, the other not— that had been killed by the sun when abnormally low tides exposed them. The corals turned gray white, as most dead corals do. When normal conditions resumed and water once more covered the dead reefs, coral larvae, the free-swimming young of deeper corals, attempted to resettle the reefs. The unpolluted reef was repopulated and thriving once more within five years. The other reef, however, fouled by oil and phosphate fertilizers spilled by ships, never recovered. As elsewhere, evidence of nature's vulnerability to pollution was proven. Ironically, the destroyed reef, a one-mile stretch with more than a hundred varieties of corals, had been previously designated a natural reserve, set aside for people to come and enjoy.

Even low levels of pollution damage the sensitive corals. Recent developments in the Red Sea are therefore ominous. Tanker traffic is increasing, and the Suez Canal is being improved to accommodate the supertankers. New oil refineries are under construction or in the planning stages. The challenge to the oil companies and to governments in the area to protect and safeguard the corals from oil spills is clear.

Natural events, too, may interfere with the growth and health of corals. Not only can

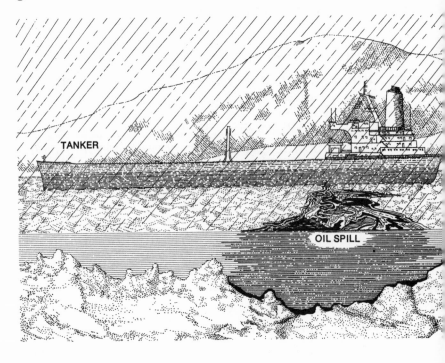

CORAL REEFS ARE VULNERABLE TO DESTRUCTION BY POLLUTION AND ACCUMULATION OF SILT.

abnormal low tides and exposure to the strong sun kill the corals, but the reefs are also vulnerable to other natural forces. Infrequent yet severe storms over the barren, reddish hills bordering the sea may cause flash floods. These rapidly formed streams rush down normally dry gullies, or wadis, carrying silt into the Red Sea. This silt accumulates, smothering and killing the corals, causing breaks in the fringing reefs. Local fishermen use these *mersas,* or small openings, as harbors.

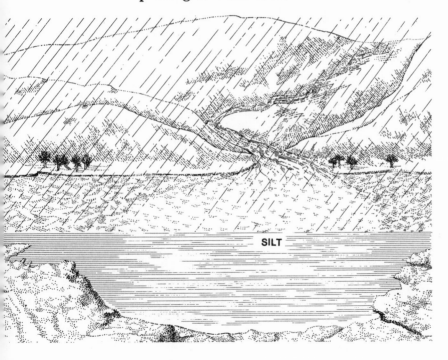

From time to time, for reasons that are not yet clear, a biological enemy of the corals, the crown-of-thorns starfish, multiplies in such numbers that large areas of coral are destroyed. This starfish species, with its long spines and many arms, feeds upon coral polyps, killing and digesting them. It leaves behind telltale white patches on the reef, which green algae eventually cover. Over a period of time, however, nature's balance is such that the corals usually recover from these natural calamities.

IV

Life on the Reef

The coral reefs of the Red Sea teem with an
array of strange and fascinating creatures. The
reefs have an enormous variety of inhabitants,
some of which cannot be found any other
place on earth. Most of these creatures have
come from the Indian Ocean; a few other species
have entered from the Mediterranean Sea
through the Suez Canal.

39

Schools of small, green damselfish, black-and white-striped humbug fish, and others of all shapes and colors swim among the coral formations. Beautifully colored butterfly fish move along in pairs. Graceful yellow-black angelfish glide by majestically. Other dazzling fish dart in and out of coral canyons, contributing to the endless movement.

A diver who explores the reefs finds a kaleidoscope of color, but there is danger also. Many reef creatures carry dangerous weapons. The elegant lion-fish displays its brightly striped, cream-and-maroon body and lacy fins. It carries some eighteen venomous spines capable of inflicting near-fatal poison. The scorpion fish and the stonefish are relatives of the lion-fish. Unlike the showy lion-fish, however, these ugly cousins disguise themselves by remaining motionless on the bottom for long periods, resembling stones or innocent bumps on the reef. But they can sting an unwary diver with their needle-sharp spines, causing severe pain and even death.

Invertebrates, creatures without backbones, also abound on the reef, crawling over it or hiding in its crevices. The jet-black sea urchins perch like giant pincushions beneath the coral ledges. Their poisonous spines, however, do not deter the beautiful triggerfish. They spurt water at the urchins, flipping them over to feed on their fleshy undersides. Red urchins with spikes as thick as pencils move about as if on stilts. Spiny starfish inch along on tiny feet, as do their relatives, the brittle stars, which resemble black, hairy spiders.

On the reef, too, are varieties of shrimps including the delicate, outlandishly patterned harlequin shrimp. This purple-spotted, white creature uses its antennae, or feelers, to turn over spiny starfish to eat their soft underparts. Exquisitely colored shell-less snails, sea slugs, sport magnificent stripes and spots. Some of these oddly shaped snails manage to steal the stinging cells from certain corals, jellyfish, and sea anemones and store them in their feathery gills for their own defense. Tube worms raise their elegant crowns of colored tentacles, like delicate feather dusters, and sweep the currents for food.

This magnificent scene of color and motion appears orderly and untroubled. But the coral reef is anything but peaceful. Space on the

HUMBUG FISH

DAMSELFISH

LION-FISH

ANGLER

STONEFISH

QUEEN ANGELFISH

ANGELFISH

SCORPION FISH

SPINY STARFISH

TUBE WORMS

BANDED CORAL SHRIMP

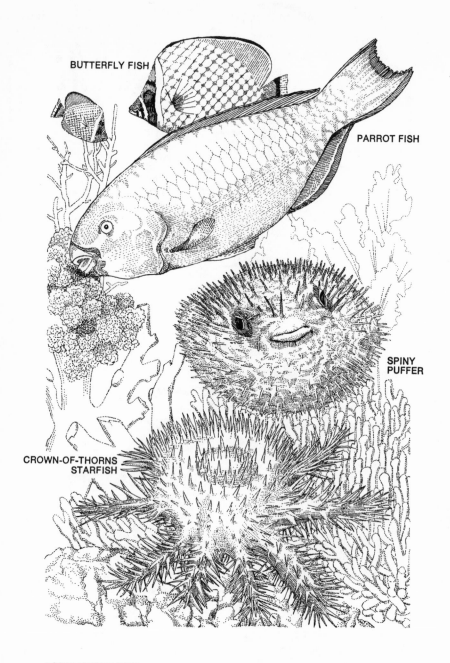

BUTTERFLY FISH

PARROT FISH

SPINY
PUFFER

CROWN-OF-THORNS
STARFISH

CORAL-EATING FISH

reef is limited and precious, so tenants must constantly defend their territories. Many reef fish are herbivores, or plant eaters; others are predators that stalk and devour fish. The larger reef dwellers, such as the giant blue-red spotted groupers, which lurk in deep caves, feed upon smaller fish. These, in turn, eat still smaller fish, shrimp, and other little animals. Large and small creatures alike are alert and wary.

In the continuous struggle for survival, even the living reef is preyed upon. Butterfly fish, sporting their disguises—dark bands that conceal their vulnerable eyes and false eyespots near their tails—poke at the coral. They use their long, narrow snouts and tweezerlike teeth to seize the fragile coral animals. The spiny puffer fish, capable of puffing itself up like a balloon to discourage enemies, uses its strong jaws to chew bits of coral.

Schools of parrot fish crunch coral with their hard parrotlike beaks. Their huge cousin, the sea rhinoceros, or bumphead, uses its humped forehead to batter the coral into bite-size pieces to get at the algae inside. As these fish chew coral they excrete sprays of fine coral sand through their gills, which then settle at the base of the reef. Sand makers like these fish produce tons of sand along the reefs of the Red Sea each year.

Strange Sea Partners

Nature has created unusual partnerships in the reef community. Certain defenseless creatures live with poisonous ones that protect them. When two different creatures associate with one another in this way for their mutual benefit, this relationship is called "symbiosis." The hermit crab and the sea anemone are such a pair. Most marine animals avoid the sea anemone because of its deadly, stinging tentacles. Hermit crabs, however, often carry one and sometimes as many as three anemones around on the backs of their borrowed shells all their lives. When the crab lodges itself in a new shell, the anemone comes right along. This relationship seems to afford the crab protection, and the anemone benefits by receiving transportation to new feeding grounds.

Certain tiny fish also associate closely with the sea anemone in a curious way. The white-spotted, black damselfish and the colorful clown fish, orange and yellow with blue-white stripes, find

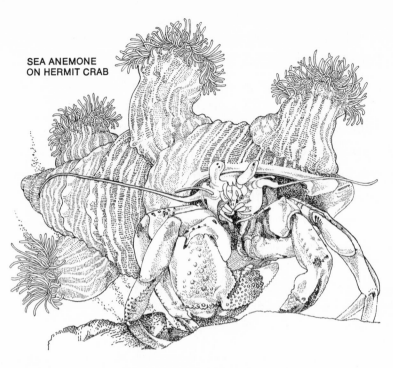

SEA ANEMONE
ON HERMIT CRAB

refuge among the anemone's poisonous
tentacles, building up a natural immunity to
them. Scientists think that the clown fish gradually
acquires this immunity by rubbing itself
against the anemone's stingers until a resistance
to their poison develops. But the fish is immune
only to the particular anemone with which it
lives, so it cannot change homes. The clown
fish may have a role in luring prey to its host,
and it also cleans house for the anemone by
removing debris and parasites from its tentacles.

47

By far the most fascinating example of symbiosis, however, involves certain enterprising tiny fish called "cleaners." The cleaner fishes, which include the neon gobyfish and the small, blue-striped wrasse, establish cleaning stations along certain parts of the reef. They set up shop, like barbers, where large fish, such as sharks, manta rays, groupers, and moray eels, come to

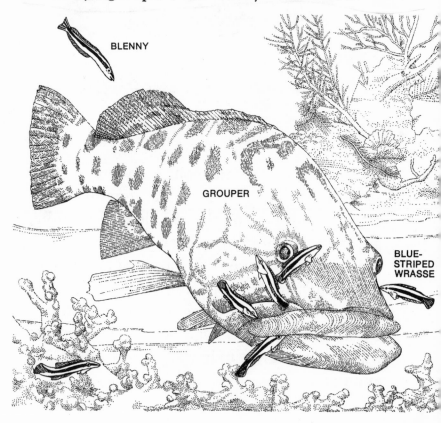

BLENNY

GROUPER

BLUE-STRIPED WRASSE

have parasites, fungi, and other pests removed.
The client fish seem to know when they are
being groomed. Sharks, for example, have been
observed raising their gill covers one at a
time as the cleaners pick over their gills.

Each cleaner is specialized and has its own
particular job. When a large fish arrives, many
cleaners go to work as a team. Each one, with

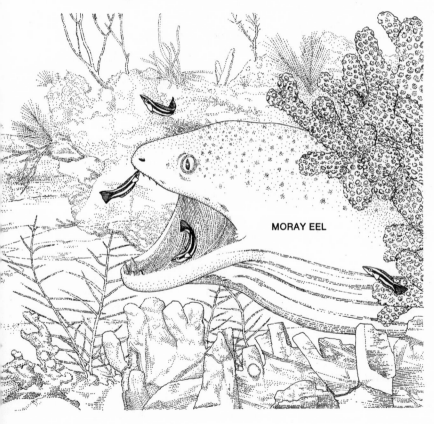

MORAY EEL

its narrow snout and tweezerlike teeth, is responsible for looking after a certain part of the fish's skin, picking off parasites and cleaning up wounds. Some of the tiny wrasses even enter the mouths of sharks and moray eels to pick parasites from between their razor-sharp teeth. This arrangement is remarkable, since the large predators do not molest the cleaners. The cleaners, in turn, thrive on the pests they consume during the grooming process.

The tiny, saw-toothed blenny fish, a mischievous creature, exploits the symbiotic relationship between the wrasses and their clients. It loiters near the cleaning station, imitating the blue-striped wrasse, which it greatly resembles. When an unsuspecting client fish allows the blenny to approach it for a cleaning, the tricky imposter instead takes a quick bite from its victim and flees.

The Reef at Night

To share the limited resources of the reef, its inhabitants are active at different times. As the light dims and darkness comes, a changeover takes place. Some fish go to sleep in the reef. Surgeonfish, with their golden tail spikes as

sharp as a surgeon's scalpels, nudge themselves
into cracks. The colorful butterfly fish find
crevices. The triggerfish, or lockfish, however,
not only wedge themselves into convenient
nooks, they lock themselves in by anchoring
a spine on their back into the coral.

Parrot fish secrete a transparent mucous sac
about themselves. This "nightgown" is thought
to protect them from detection by the moray
eel. The moray eel is a predator that leaves its
den in the reef at night to hunt using its
keen sense of smell. This eel can inflict severe
wounds and has a reputation among some
experienced divers as one of the most dangerous
animals in the Red Sea.

With darkness, other fish, however, become
active in the reef as the night feeders take over.
Schools of reddish squirrelfish with large
buttonlike eyes seem especially well adapted to
the dim light. These frisky creatures chirp like
their namesakes when disturbed. Slender,
little cardinal fish, which hide during the day by
standing on their heads among the spines of
large sea urchins, emerge and begin to feed.

One of the most striking night reef animals is
the strange brittle star, or basket starfish. At

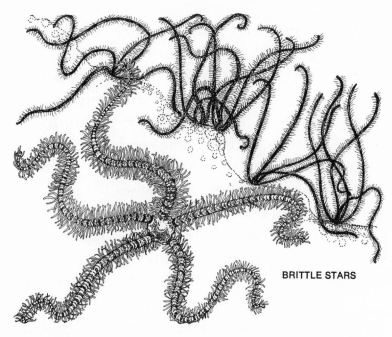

BRITTLE STARS

dusk, this eerie creature emerges from its home among the corals to creep to its feeding station. There it unfolds its many delicate, fernlike arms, which have earned for it the name Gorgon's head, after a monster in Greek mythology, whose head was covered by snakes. These fragile, feathery extensions have hooks to catch food, and they coil up to pass it into the mouth. Each morning at dawn the brittle star descends once more into its home in the reef. It returns each night for months to the same feeding station. Well-known ocean-

ographer Jacques Costeau, who has explored
the Red Sea, was fascinated by this creature. He
nicknamed it the "walking bush."

Beyond the Reef

Life in the Rea Sea is not confined to the coral
reefs. Over the reef and beyond it, startling
displays of blue-green lights are common at night.
These colored lights are produced by tiny
organisms called "plankton," which are abundant
in the surface water after darkness and glow
when disturbed.

Beneath the clear water beyond the reef are
sandy bottom stretches. Unlike the reef, where
colorful fish bustle about, the sea bottom seems
empty. The fish and other animals here are
harder to find because in large open areas
they use camouflage to survive.

The sea cucumber, which Arab fishermen hunt
in shallower water, looks as if it were part of
the sea bottom, as it slowly inches along filtering
plankton with its crown of hairy tentacles.
It is a brown, tube-shaped creature, which may
grow up to two feet long. A sticky, poisonous
mucous coats its skin, which bristles with short,
white spikes, its defenses against attack. The

cucumber spurts out its gooey inner organs to entrap its enemies when threatened.

Plants exist on the sea floor, but what look like clumps of algae may be deceiving. These clumps may be anglerfish. Garbed in its green disguise, this irregularly shaped fish is well camouflaged. It is a cunning creature, which earns its name by the way it fishes for its food. From a spine on its forehead, the anglerfish dangles a fleshy lure resembling a worm. Fish that are fooled by the false bait try to eat it and are suddenly

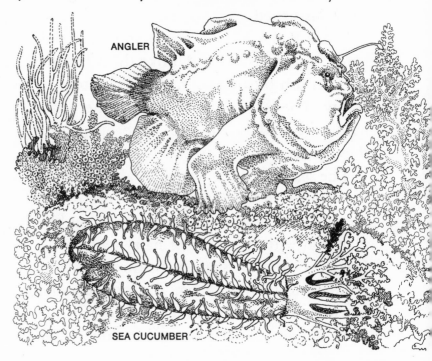

ANGLER

SEA CUCUMBER

SOME CREATURES USE CAMOUFLAGE TO SURVIVE.

sucked into the angler's gaping mouth. Should
the clever anglerfish lose its bait to its prey,
it merely grows another.

A field of sea grass at the bottom of the Red Sea
may also not be as empty as it first appears.
Curious little sea horses and their relatives, the
slender, finger-long pipefish, hide out among
the waving fronds. Swarms of silvery gray eels,
sometimes as many as 5000 in a single colony,
stand on end eerily swaying in the currents like
blades of grass. These fish are only about as thick

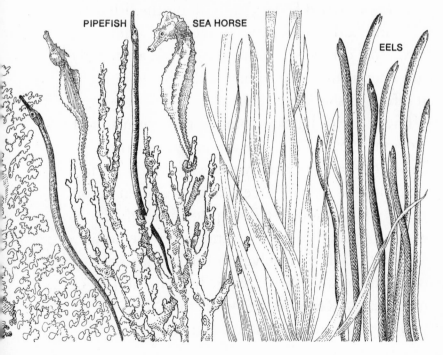

PIPEFISH SEA HORSE EELS

as a finger and may reach three feet in length. A colony of feeding eels so much resembles a garden of sea grass that these wary creatures have been named the garden eels.

Another creature that conceals itself in the sandy sea floor is currently attracting the attention of marine scientists. It is the Moses sole, a small, speckled, sandy-colored fish. This flat fish, unique to the Red Sea, has aroused interest because it produces a substance that may repel sharks. The repellent appears to be a milky secretion released from glands along the fish's back and tail fins. If the secretion of the Moses sole can be synthesized, or made artificially with chemicals, science may at last have found an effective shark repellent.

The Red Sea harbors some of the world's most ferocious sharks. They occasionally visit the sea bottom but are usually seen close to the surface, searching for prey. These sharks are often accompanied by foot-long, striped pilot fish, which swim alongside the sharks, and by the remoras, fish that attach themselves to the shark's belly by means of an oval sucking disc on the top of their heads. Remoras and pilot fish may receive protection by associating with sharks

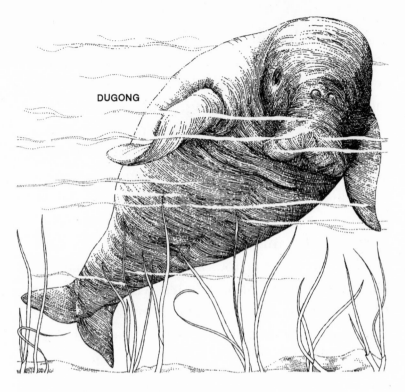

DUGONG

and may gain small bits of their catch. In
return, these fish seem to clean away the
parasites of sharks. Pilot fish and remoras also
accompany other large fish, boats, and even
people. Red Sea divers have reported pilot
fish hovering about their masks and remoras
picking at their chests, apparently hunting
for parasites.

Mammals also swim in the warm, salty waters
of the Red Sea. The gray dugong, or sea cow,

is a strange-looking animal. It is a large, bulky creature that lives in the sea and grazes on vegetation. The gentle dugong, like other mammals, nurses its young. With her newborn calf, the mother dugong rises to the surface, lifting it above the water to breathe. This behavior may account for the legends about mermaids. Lonely sailors spying the shy dugong nursing its baby in the distance may have mistaken the animal for a mermaid.

Swimming here, too, are other mammals. Dolphins frolic; pilot whales whistle and chirp to one another. And at certain times of the year, the great sperm whales visit the Red Sea from the Indian Ocean.

V

Mineral Resources

In the fall of 1964, a British research vessel aptly
named *Discovery* was cruising southward
toward the Indian Ocean from Suez. It was in
the center of the Red Sea, west of Saudi Arabia's
port city of Jiddah. Curious about reports
from previous research expeditions in 1948,
1958, and 1963 that there were peculiar warm
and salty waters deep below the surface in this

area, scientists aboard the ship decided to investigate. They lowered special bottles equipped with temperature gauges thousands of feet into the sea to sample water from the depths and soon made an extraordinary discovery.

"We found it hard to believe the thermometers when the bottles came up," reported the chief scientist of the expedition, Doctor John Swallow. Instead of the cooler temperatures one would normally find at great depths, their instruments recorded the presence of warm water registering 111 degrees Fahrenheit just above the bottom, more than a mile below. These waters proved to be about 40 degrees hotter than the rest of the Red Sea and nearly seven times saltier.

The oceanographers had discovered a deep, hot brine pool, eight square miles in area, at the center of the Red Sea. Brine is water saturated with salt and is heavier than ordinary seawater. Though warm water generally rises, the density of hot brine holds it down. The scientists decided to name the pool Discovery Deep in honor of their ship. They were pleased with their find, although they were unsuccessful in attempts to raise samples of the sediments lying beneath the pool.

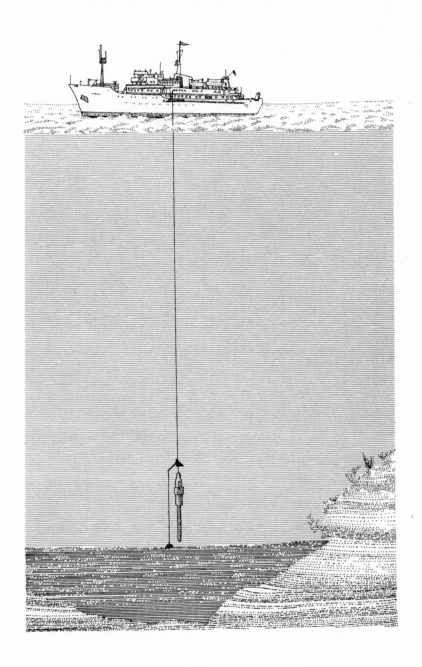

DISCOVERY INVESTIGATES THE DEPTHS OF THE RED SEA.

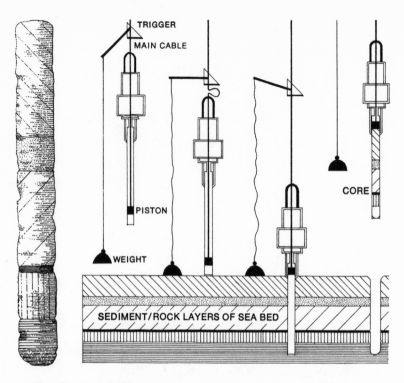

Early the following year, the *Atlantis II,* a research vessel from the Woods Hole Oceanographic Institution in Massachusetts, was sailing through the Red Sea on its way to the Indian Ocean. Though engine trouble and other problems had put them four days behind schedule, the researchers, excited by the earlier findings, paused to see if they could obtain samples from the bottom of the Discovery Deep. They lowered corer machines for this purpose

and raised hot, black ooze that looked
like tar from the bottom. Their vessel, however,
had drifted northward five miles away from
the Discovery Deep. Accidentally they had
found another deep brine pool larger than the
first. They named this salty basin the Atlantis II
Deep. It proved to be about fifty miles square,
and its waters were even hotter, 133 degrees
Fahrenheit.

But what of the strange black sediment?
Though the *Atlantis II* was a research vessel, it
was not outfitted with the instruments and
necessary agents for complicated chemical analysis.
The determined team borrowed a large cauldron
from the galley and raided the pantry, the
photography darkroom, and even the sick bay
for chemicals from which they ingeniously made
crude testing agents. They began an analysis
of the sediment. When the ship docked at
Aden, at the southern entrance of the Red Sea,
the scientists were granted permission to use
the chemistry laboratory of a small college in the
desert. There they completed their analysis
and made an amazing finding. The brine
and the underlying dark ooze contained
extremely rich concentrations of valuable metals.

The discovery of hot brine pools rich in metal deposits at the bottom of the Red Sea now began to stir considerable interest. Researchers from the Woods Hole Institution and guest scientists from Scripps Institution of Oceanography, Massachusetts Institute of Technology, Cambridge (England), and Göteberg (Sweden) formed a team to study the brine pools. They sailed aboard the *Chain* from Woods Hole the following fall, in 1966. In the brine-pool region at the center of the Red Sea, they discovered a third pool less than two miles square, which they named the Chain Deep. The scientists raised cores of layered sediment from beneath this pool and from other deeps.

"Probably man has never seen a more colorful sedimentary product emerge from the depths of the sea. The color variation is fantastic; all shades of white, black, red, green, blue or yellow can be observed," commented geologists David A. Ross and Egon T. Degens. The sediment colors were similar to, though more brilliant than, those found in Indian paintings and Mexican rugs, according to these investigators.

The brine pools lie at the bottom of a deep crack called a "rift," which runs lengthwise

64

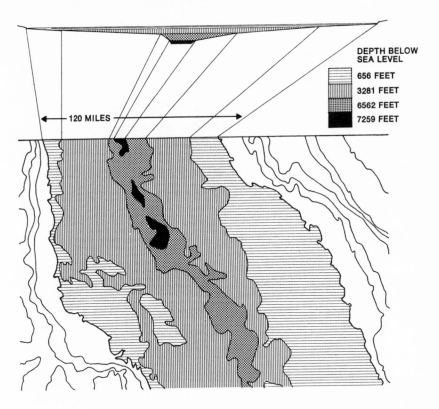

DEPTH BELOW
SEA LEVEL

656 FEET
3281 FEET
6562 FEET
7259 FEET

120 MILES

up the center of the Red Sea. The pools hold one
of the richest concentrations of heavy metals
known to exist on earth. Some of these elements
are found there in quantities 50,000 times
greater than are present normally in seawater.
Based on outdated 1968 estimates, the value
of copper, gold, silver, and zinc found in the
upper layers of sediment from the Atlantis II
Deep alone exceeded $2.4 billion. Iron

and manganese deposits make this lode even more valuable.

News of these findings interested more than the scientific community. Enterprising individuals and governments were now attracted. Their interest was further aroused when scientists announced in 1971 that additional studies had revealed the Atlantis II Deep to be growing warmer and larger. It was already 2.7 degrees hotter than it had been five years earlier, and the rich sediment was increasing.

The question of ownership of this vast undersea treasure became increasingly important. Did it belong to neighboring countries? Or was it in international waters, beyond the territorial rights of Sudan to the west and Saudi Arabia to the east? Did the treasure belong to the whole world? In 1967, the United Nations delegate from Malta proposed that the United Nations assume jurisdiction over the mineral resources of all international waters.

Ordinarily it is not practical to extract minerals from the sediments beneath the sea because they are usually present only in minute quantities. But John E. Crawford, head of a sea-mining company in California, believed that the unusually heavy concentration of minerals in the brine pools in the Red Sea might make them an exception. He hoped to learn how to mine these minerals and to sell this knowledge to nations and companies that could afford to go ahead and do the actual mining. Crawford believed the pools in the Red Sea were in international waters, and he sought the right to explore them. In 1968, he asked the United Nations to grant him a lease to conduct tests in the brine-pool area. But the United Nations replied that it had no authority to grant mineral rights to the Red Sea floor. Crawford's request was unique and unprecedented. Mining the sea floor was so new that the United States Government didn't have a form to honor such a request. The United Nations, however, continued to debate the Malta proposal. These discussions led to a series of important international meetings, the Law of the Sea Conferences.

Valuable minerals have been discovered not only at the bottom of the Red Sea but elsewhere as well. If peaceful and equitable terms can be arranged between nations to extract precious nodules of nickel, copper, cobalt, and manganese from the Pacific Ocean and from other seabeds as well, then the treasures of the Red Sea may be made available to humanity also. In a world where the supply of natural mineral resources is shrinking there is additional pressure for ores. The sea could satisfy a good part of this demand.

VI

An Ocean Being Born

While some consider how to exploit the mineral
riches, the hot brine pools at the bottom of the
Red Sea continue to attract the interest of
scientists for other reasons. One of their dis-
coverers, Doctor David Ross, has stated:
"The value of these deposits on the sea floor,
although high, is not the most important aspect
here. It is that we have found a process occurring

69

from which we can learn more about the formation of mineral deposits on land and the origin of the ocean basins." The existence of sediments rich in metals in the center of the Red Sea is linked to activities occurring deep within the earth. The ores are clues to the origin of the Red Sea.

Many scientists today believe a new theory about the earth's history called "plate tectonics." This theory holds that the continents, together with the floor of the oceans, form huge blocks of rock called "plates." These plates are about one hundred miles thick, and there are some twenty of them, differing in size. They cover the surface of the planet like giant ice floes and are in constant slow motion. Traveling about an inch or two a year, they may move together or pull apart.

Where the plates collide, the edges may be thrust upward to form great mountain ranges. Or the edges may overlap, and the underlying piece break off and be forced downward, melting in the hot, molten interior of the earth. Where pieces are pushed downward, deep ocean trenches are formed. Elsewhere, when plates meet, their edges may grind and rub. In all these areas earthquakes are common. When plates move apart, their spreading is associated with volcanic activity along the line of separation, and hot lava from the earth's molten core rises to fill the crack.

If you look at a globe, a map, or the photographs taken from spacecraft or orbiting satellites, you will see how the Arabian and African coastlines almost match like pieces in a jigsaw puzzle. Some scientists who study the earth's outer crust think that about 200 million years ago, all the continents were joined together to form one great landmass or supercontinent, which they named Pangaea. At that time, the dinosaurs ruled the land, and fish swam in the single, huge, surrounding ocean.

Very slowly over eons of time, the great landmass split into continental plates, and the plates began to spread apart. Slowly they moved toward their present positions. By about eighty-five million years ago, the earth's surface began to look very much as it does today. The shifting of the plates had caused the Rocky Mountains, the Andes, and the great Himalayas to thrust up. As the dinosaurs began to disappear, birds and mammals were starting to flourish, and

71

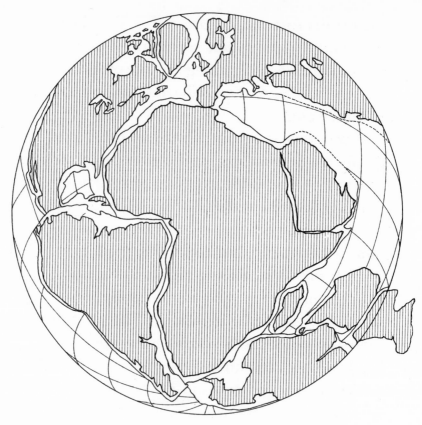

the great grassy plains had developed. Then, about twenty million years ago, long before man appeared, the plate upon which the Arabian peninsula sits began to move away from the African plate. This separation created a gap. The gap widened and deepened, and Indian Ocean water flowed in. The birth of the Red Sea had begun.

72

When the Red Sea was born, it was only a narrow slit of water and grew slowly with time. About two million years ago it began to widen at a faster rate, and a rift, running lengthwise up the center of the Red Sea, opened. It is the same deep crack upon which the brine pools lie. Molten lava from the earth's interior welled up to fill the crack. As the lava hardened, it formed a new sea floor, pushing the older sea floor to the side.

This rifting process and the sea-floor spreading that accompanies it is still going on. It is the process by which oceans widen. About one square mile of new ocean floor is created each year throughout the earth's oceans. The Red Sea widens about one inch yearly. But the earth does not have to stretch to fit in this addition. As new ocean floor forms beside one ocean rift, an equal amount of floor is thought to disappear elsewhere into a deep, undersea trench. According to Doctor Ross, if the rifting process and sea-floor spreading continue, the Red Sea could in a few hundred million years attain a width as great as that of the Atlantic Ocean today.

How can scientists make such predictions? The answer lies in knowledge that is being

developed through scientific techniques.
Sonar and other electronic devices, undersea
photography, and drilling and coring methods
are enabling researchers around the world to
chart the ocean floor. As data accumulates,
an amazing picture of the underwater surface has
begun to emerge. Vast sprawling plains, deep
ocean trenches, mountain chains, and strange,
flat-topped sea mountains are being discovered.
Most startling of all, scientists describe a mountain
chain that snakes its way 40,000 miles around
the world through the center of all the oceans,
like the seam on a softball. This mountain
chain is split by a rift.

This mid-ocean rift system does something
quite unusual in the southwestern corner of the
Red Sea. It rises up out of the water onto
the land in a wild, barren part of Ethiopia known
as the Afar Triangle. There it meets the rift
that extends up the center of the Red Sea through
the Gulf of Aqaba northeastward to northern
Syria. It also intersects a rift system that
stretches from the Afar Triangle southward
into East Africa.

The desolate Afar Triangle, where these three
great cracks in the earth's surface meet, is

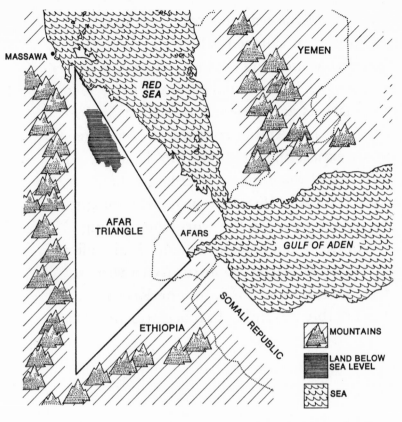

wracked by earthquakes and volcanic eruptions.
It has attracted geologists from France, Italy,
and the United States. They have discovered
that part of the Triangle had once been
underwater, an ancient arm of the Red Sea.
Volcanic eruptions are thought to have created
mountains that cut the Triangle off from
the sea and pushed it temporarily above sea level.

Evaporation of the seawater over ages has
left behind great salt beds. These beds attract
the Danakil, wandering nomads, who come to
mine this salt. Their camel caravans carry it to
distant markets across northeast Africa.

As Africa and Arabia continue to separate,
scientists expect that one day the Triangle will
be submerged once more to enlarge the
Red Sea. The Afar Triangle provides geologists
a rare chance to study the worldwide rifting
process of the ocean bottom on land. It also affords
them an extraordinary opportunity to witness
the way oceans are created, for the Red Sea
is a remarkable example of an ocean being born.

Index

* indicates illustration

Aden, Gulf, 12, 13*, 16
Afar Triangle, 74-76, 75*
Africa, 23, 24-25*, 76
algae, 12-13, 29, 38, 45, 54
Aqaba, Gulf, 12, 13*, 22, 35, 74
Arabia, 16, 26, 76
Asia, 12, 26
Atlantis II, 62-63

Bab-el-Mandeb, Straits, 12, 27
brine, 60, 63, 64, 69
brittle stars, 41, 51, 52*

California, 12, 66
Canaan, 22
corals, 11, 28-32, 30*, 33*, 40, 41; polyp, 29, 38

77

Cousteau, Jacques, 53
currents, 11

Discovery, 58-60, 61*

East Africa, 12, 16, 74
Egypt, 12, 13*, 14, 15-20, 24
Elat, 22, 35
Ethiopia, 12, 13*, 74, 75*
Exodus, 20, 22

fish, angel-, 40, 42*; angler,
    42*, 54*-55; blenny, 48*,
    50; butterfly, 40, 42*, 45,
    51; clown-, 46-47,
    damsel-, 40, 42*, 46;
    goby-, 48; grouper, 45,
    48*; humbug, 40, 42*;
    jelly-, 29, 41; lion-, 40,
    42*; manta ray, 48;
    moray eel, 48*, 50, 51;
    parrot, 44*, 45, 51;
    puffer, 44*, 45; scorpion,
    40, 42*; shark, 48, 49, 50,
    56-57; star-, 38, 41, 42*,
    44*; stone-, 40, 42*;
    surgeon-, 50; trigger-, 41,
    42*, 51; wrasse, 48*, 50

Gibraltar, Straits, 24

Hatshepsut, 16, 17*

Hebrews, 20-22, 21*
hermit crab, 46, 47*
Herodotus, 24
history, 15-26, 17*, 18*,
    21*, 25*

Indian Ocean, 12, 13*, 16,
    27, 39, 58, 59, 62
Israel, 22

khamsin, 12

Lebanon, 22
limestone, 34

mammals, 57*-58
Mediterranean Sea, 12,
    13*, 22, 23, 24, 26, 39
mineral rights, 66-67
Moses, 14, 20, 21*

Necho, 23-24
Nile, 22, 23

oil, 36*
Ophir, 22-23

Palermo Stone, 16
Phoenicians, 22, 24
plankton, 53
plate tectonics, 70-73, 72*
pollutants, 35-36*

Punt, 16-19, 23

Reed Sea, 20-22, 21*
reefs, 11, 32-35, 33*, 41

Sahure, 16
salinity, 28
Saudi Arabia, 12, 13*, 59, 66
sea anemone, 29, 41, 46, 47*
sea cucumber, 53-54
sea urchin, 40-41, 42*, 51
Sheba, Queen of, 23
shrimp, 41
snail, 41
Solomon, King, 22-23

Sudan, 12, 13*, 32, 66
Suez Canal, 12, 20, 23, 26, 36, 39
Suez, Gulf, 12, 13*, 59
symbiosis, 46-50, 47*, 48*, 56-57
Syria, 22, 74

temperature, 12, 28, 60
Thebes, 17
tube worms, 41, 42*

United Nations, 66, 67

Yemen, 12, 13*, 23

About the Author

Francine Jacobs was born in New York City and has a B.A. in Education from Queens College. She has taught in the elementary grades in Rye, New York, and also conducted a reading-enrichment program in Chappaqua, New York. Now she concentrates on writing children's books, a number of which are on nature-science subjects. Mrs. Jacobs and her husband live in Westchester County. They have two children, a son and a daughter.

About the Artist

Elsie Wrigley was born in Bolton, England, and attended the Manchester Regional College of Art. A teacher as well as an illustrator, Mrs. Wrigley taught at different schools before and after her marriage. Since 1960 she has concentrated on illustration and writing, publishing her first children's story in 1966.

Mr. and Mrs. Wrigley now live in Devon.